Marta's Cupcake Problem

by Carrie Smith • illustrated by Anita DuFalla

Marta and her mom
were at the store.

Marta's mom saw some cupcakes.

"Your birthday is coming up,
Marta," she said.

"Would you like to take cupcakes
to school?"

CUPCAKES

VANILLA CHOCOLATE VANILLA CHOCOLATE
VANILLA CHOCOLATE VANILLA CHOCOLATE
VANILLA CHOCOLATE VANILLA CHOCOLATE
VANILLA CHOCOLATE VANILLA CHOCOLATE
VANILLA CHOCOLATE VANILLA CHOCOLATE
VANILLA CHOCOLATE VANILLA CHOCOLATE
VANILLA CHOCOLATE VANILLA CHOCOLATE
VANILLA CHOCOLATE VANILLA CHOCOLATE

"Yes!" said Marta.

"But which cupcakes do I take?

Chocolate or vanilla?"

Marta's mom did not know.

Marta made a chart.
She would ask her friends
which cupcakes they liked.

Marta went up to Ben at school.
"Ben, which do you like?
Chocolate or vanilla?"

"I like vanilla," said Ben.
Marta put his name on her chart.

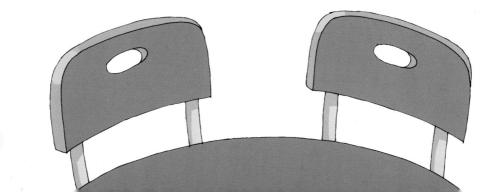

Marta went up to Ava and Dan.
"Which do you like?
Chocolate or vanilla?"

"I like vanilla," said Ava.

"I like chocolate," said Dan.
Marta put their names
on her chart.

Marta asked everybody
in her class. She put
their names on her chart.

Chocolate	Vanilla
1. Marta	1. Ben
2. Dan	2. Ava
3. Emma	3. Billy
4. Jan	

Marta took her chart home.
"I know which cupcakes
to get," she told her mom.
"We need 12 vanilla cupcakes.
We need 8 chocolate cupcakes."

15

Marta took her cupcakes
to school. Everybody was happy.
They all got cupcakes they liked!